Ollie Knappett.
With lov.

.ut

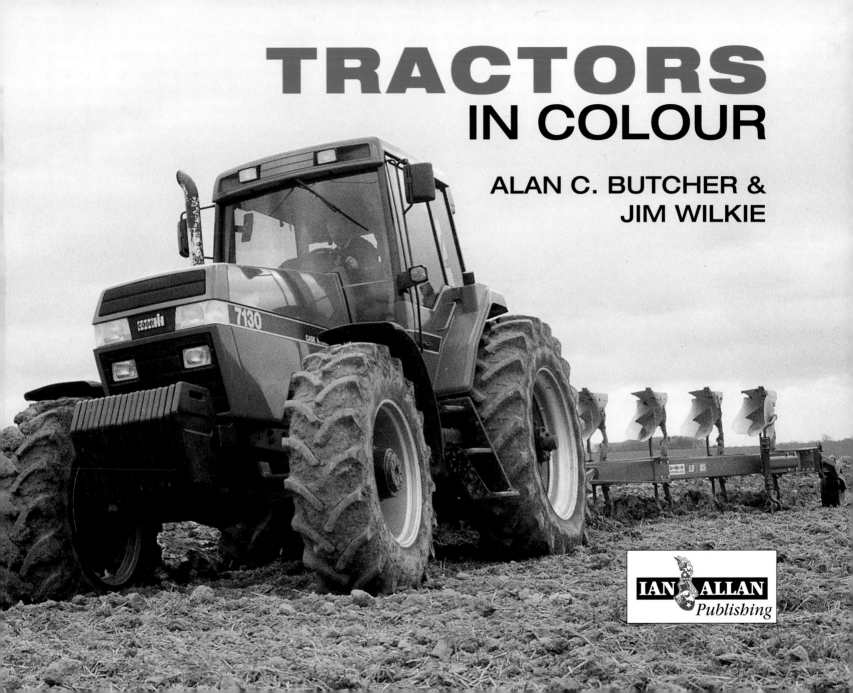

TRACTORS
IN COLOUR

ALAN C. BUTCHER &
JIM WILKIE

IAN ALLAN
Publishing

First published 1996

ISBN 0 7110 2246 1

Published by Ian Allan Publishing

an imprint of Ian Allan Ltd, Terminal House,
Station Approach, Shepperton, Surrey TW17 8AS;
and printed by Ian Allan Printing Ltd,
Coombelands House, Coombelands Lane,
Addlestone, Surrey KT15 1HY.

Photographs credited to ACB were taken by the author.

Dedication
To Rachel and Lucy.

Front cover: *With a 100 turbocharged horsepower
at his command the driver of the Massey 390T will
make quick work of springtime stubble cultivation.
This will start preparations for the next crop.*
Massey Ferguson

Back cover: *The driver of this six cylinder Ford 8210
is still making good progress with his Ransomes
reversible plough. One hundred years ago this
landscape would have been dotted with horse teams
at work. Fifty years ago you would probably have
been able to spot several tractors at work. Now one
driver and a modern tractor does all the work.*
Peter Adams

Title page: *A Case 7130 is seen pulling a reversible
plough.* Peter Adams

Introduction

For centuries the land has been farmed for food crops. With the coming of the Industrial Revolution a method had to be found to increase production to sustain the growing population. The harnessing of steam power was a great advance, but few farmers could afford their own equipment so the sight of steam engines and associated equipment being towed around the countryside from farm to farm became a common sight. The problem with this was that no matter how hard one tried the race was always on to harvest the crops at their best and beat the weather.

The coming of the internal combustion engine saw a radical change to the farmers' way of life. Here at last was a mechanical means to both plough the ground and harvest the crops when the time was ripe and not have to wait whilst the steam engines paraded around the countryside. It was however, not an overnight change.

As the use of the tractor spread, so more manufacturers appeared on the scene as they perceived a market for their products. Over the ensuing 100 years manufacturers have come, merged, and in a number of cases gone. In the early 1980s there were well over 100 manufacturers world-wide. They supplied everything from small agricultural machines to large prairie tractors.

It is not intended that this book should give but a very brief background to either the manufacturers or the models illustrated. Therefore I have decided to illustrate tractors, both old and new, to give a brief insight into the rally scene and work in the fields.

Alan C. Butcher   Scarning 1996

Left: *Four-wheel drive provides sufficient traction for this modern Massey Ferguson to work on Padstow beach at low tide, whilst in the process of 'dredging' for sea sand. A tractor and trailer can often be a sensible alternative to a specialist dumper. Both tractor and trailer have many other uses in the course of the year. The front mudguards are provided to reduce the road spray on the cab glass.* ACB

Below: *Row crop versions of the Fordson N were produced in small numbers. John Deere supplied their well-proved Model A to do the same job.*

Ivel Agricultural Motor

In 1902 Dan Albone patented his 'Agricultural Motor'. This was no paper invention; by 1903 it was in regular production. Indeed an armoured version had even been demonstrated to the War Office. The Ivel developed 20 brake horsepower at 850rpm and weighed only 32cwt (1,650kg). Little more development was carried out after his death in 1906. Even so by 1914 Ivel Tractors from the Biggleswade, Bedfordshire factory were at work in Brazil, New Zealand, Russia, and France. By 1920 the company was in receivership and the Ivel regarded as outdated. Had Dan Albone lived, with his energy and innovation who knows how the British tractor industry would have developed?

Dan Albone's lasting legacy was that he had demonstrated to sceptical farmers that 'agricultural motors' would be the power source of the future. His tractor company was commercially successful in its own right and not just as a department of an existing successful company. Future tractor manufacturers owed him a big debt as he had prepared the market for tractors.

Dan Albone and his son (front right) *at an early demonstration of the Ivel in 1903. Ploughing was a two-man job using a modified horse plough. Many features of the Ivel would reappear in later designs. The chain drive to the steering wheel would be inspired by Albone's cycling background.* Biggleswade History Society

Rumley Oil Pull

Rumley of Indiana concentrated on manufacturing sturdy tractors. It was their practice to understate the power of their products. As a result their tractors acquired a reputation for sustained pulling. The 'Oil Pull' referred to the fact they would deliver their rated power on cheap fuel rather than refined petrol. Bad debts on overseas sales to Russia crippled the company and they were taken over by Allis Chalmers a firm of millwrights that were creating a tractor division.

This 1927 example was imported by a collector. It is thanks to such collectors that it is possible to see these unusual makes at some rallies and museums. ACB

Allis Chalmers U

Low pressure rubber tyres transformed tractor design in the 1930s. They had sufficient grip for field work, yet could be used on the road. Ride was improved for the driver and vibration reduced. More of the engine's power could be utilised for work. Gear ratios could be chosen to give a faster top speed perhaps nine or ten miles an hour rather than three or four.

The U was the first tractor to offer low pressure pneumatic tyres as a regular option. A high speed top gear was fitted which was only for use when rubber tyres were fitted. For advertising purposes a few high geared tractors were built. On one, in 1933, Barney Oldfield set a new tractor speed record of 64.28mph! More significantly the introduction of pneumatic tyres made it possible to use the same tractor for road and field work.

The Allis Chalmers U was the first tractor designed for rubber tyres. The example seen here still has the first simple tread pattern. Even that has been sufficient to pull an 8 tonne load. Incidentally the 1939 single deck SOS/SON alongside RC7927 is still in revenue earning service. Its original owners Trent rescued it in 1978, disused, from a farm yard. It once again has a full Certificate of Fitness and is a popular hire for special occasions. Not bad after 55 years. A. F. Porter

Allis Chalmers M

Fitting tracks to a wheeled tractor made a very cost effective way of building a crawler tractor. The Monarch Tractor Co had specialised in crawlers prior to AC taking them over. A crawler tractor could use the full power of the engine at a slower forward speed than a wheeled tractor. Thus crawlers tended to be used for heavy jobs where the power was required. On most soils a crawler could do useful work when a wheel tractor got stuck stuck.

The M crawler shows it is obviously based on the U featured on the previous page. It is waiting to resume ploughing in a vintage class when the opening 'split' has been judged. Eric Sawford

Allis Chalmers HD7

Crawler users soon realised that a tracked machine could use far more power than a wheeled tractor. Selecting a General Motors blown two stroke diesel engine offered increased power. This HD7 had roughly twice the power of an M. Its operating weight was also doubled. The distinctive note of the engine was far more raucous than the refined smoothness of the M. By 1940 crawlers were becoming more powerful than any wheel tractor that could be sold, so designs were becoming more specialised. Many Allis Chalmers HD7s started life with the American Forces.

This example shows how the stylists influence was at work on most American designs by 1940. ACB

Allis Chalmers B

The outbreak of war lead to a big increase in the area of land devoted to growing potatoes.

The policy of importing cheap food had left Britain's food stocks vulnerable to attacks on shipping. Because of their high moisture content home-grown potatoes would save shipping space and bulk out the daily food ration.

The only problem was that many more farmers would have to grow them. This created a need for tractors able to cultivate between the rows. America had pioneered this type of tractor so was the logical source. Allis Chalmers could offer their compact B which proved satisfactory.

As can be seen, the narrow transmission tunnel allowed the driver to look down on to mid-mounted implements. When hoeing between rows this gave precise control. As a result many Bs led long and useful lives. ACB

9

Allis Chalmers

The final British-built Allis Chalmers was the ED40. Introduced in 1960 it was intended to be a more general purpose tractor. Power was provided by a Standard 23C engine previously used in the first Ferguson 35s. The ED40 faced stiff competition from other makes and by 1965, it had faded away.

In 1985 Allis Chalmers was bought by KHD of Germany and merged with their Deutz tractor business.

Whilst being a serviceable tractor the ED40 did not have sufficient appeal to ensure good sales. Whilst quite striking, the styling was not enough. ACB

Caterpillar 22

Few tractor names are better known than Caterpillar. From their beginnings in 1904 their speciality has always been the tracklaying or crawler tractor. Tracks give maximum traction for engine power and light tread on difficult ground conditions. Their main disadvantage comes when the tractor needs to travel along public roads. Unlike other crawler manufacturers Caterpillar did not have a wheeled alternative to offer. As a result they were particularly good at finding novel applications for tracked tractors.

This 1936 22 is fitted with a Caterpillar-built spark ignition engine. It was restored after being discarded in a quarry by the previous owner. ACB

Caterpillar D2

The D2 developed from the 22 but was fitted with Caterpillar's specially developed diesel engine. To overcome the problem of unreliable starting, a small petrol donkey engine is fitted. This is started with a rope pull, and once running it drives the main engine. This allows the lubrication oil to circulate whilst the petrol engine warms the coolant in the engine. Only then is the diesel fuel turned on and the main engine started up. Whilst this sounds long-winded, it means minimum wear on the engine when starting from cold and there is no need to fit an electrical system. There are still farms where a D2 is held in reserve for difficult conditions.

The Caterpillar D2 pictured is fitted with street plates. These have to be fitted on the tracks to reduce the damage caused when running on public roads. Eric Sawford

Caterpillar Challenger

The latest Caterpillars are fitted with rubber tracks. Although they still steer like conventional tracks they can be used on public roads. As a result, on most ground conditions, they offer the best of four-wheel drive and crawler performance. Rubber tracks are also to be found on a few big trailers in use in vegetable-growing areas. By spreading the weight over a greater surface area the tracks can travel over soft ground. Compared with the squeals and clanks of conventional tracks, the most striking impression is the silence and the high forward speed that is possible.

The power of this Challenger allows it to run with both tracks on unploughed ground. As well as giving better grip the driver gets a level ride. The rubber tracks always draw an interested audience when they are demonstrated.
Tony Ash

David Brown VAK 1

It was Harry Ferguson that got David Brown into tractor manufacture. He persuaded 'young' David to manufacture a revolutionary new design of tractor for his marketing company. Production commenced in 1936 at Meltham near Huddersfield. In 1938 Ferguson went to Ford of America, but David Brown engineers felt they could produce a better tractor without Ferguson's help.

Although launched in 1939, the demands of war work meant production was still restricted when this example was made in 1945. ACB

David Brown VIG

One model introduced during the war was the
Industrial version VIG. Often fitted with a
winch they were frequently used for aircraft
towing. Indeed some were fitted with fluid
flywheels to give a more gentle move away
under load. The mudguards are of heavy plate
with cast iron ballast tucked away underneath.
Later some of these saw further service
extracting timber, shunting trailers and —
with a belt pulley fitted — as threshing
tractors. Many later agricultural models were
available modified for airfield use.

*This stylish Industrial version (right-hand
tractor) is fitted with a winch. The left-hand
tractor is a Field Marshall IIIA in the livery
adopted by Marshall and Fowler around
1954.* ACB

*The ample front
mudguards on
the VIG
protected the
driver from road
spray. They also
served as extra
ballast to
increase the
tractor's weight.
Fifty years later
the advantages
of mudguards
over the front
wheels are
becoming more
generally
recognised.* ACB

David Brown Cropmaster

The VAK 1 became the Cropmaster. The raised windshield was retained to divert cold winds away from the driver's hands and legs. At least one farmer took advantage of the extra wide bench seat provided to take his new bride on honeymoon by Cropmaster! Other drivers trained their dogs to ride alongside them. By this time David Brown was offering diesel power. From the beginning the original spark ignition engine design had been planned strong enough for a later diesel version. As a result David Brown was the first British tractor maker to offer its own make of diesel engine.

(Left) Cropmaster and (right) Super Cropmaster with bigger engine and tyres. Additional weights for extra grip are bolted to the rear wheels. ACB

David Brown 50 TD

David Brown first built crawler tractors during the World War 2. On certain soils, tracks reduced the pressure imposed, so cultivation could start sooner and go on longer. At slower speeds tracks had far more pull than rubber tyres. Track repairs could be costly. The other big disadvantage of any crawler was the damage they caused to public roads.

David Brown's last tracklayer model was the 50 TD (pictured right) introduced in 1952. This was powered by a six cylinder version of the David Brown diesel engine. A 1950 Cropmaster (pictured left) fitted with the newly introduced optional diesel engine. ACB

David Brown 2D

Although launched in 1956 as a light general purpose tractor, most buyers of the David Brown 2D were market gardeners. Some are still using them. The rear-mounted two cylinder engine meant the driver had an almost unobstructed view of the underslung implements.

Compressed air was used to lift and lower them. Precision hoeing was easily achieved. Although production of the 2D stopped in 1961 David Brown was still a successful company when purchased by Tenneco in 1972.

This is the particularly compact vineyard model. ACB

The Austin

During World War 1 Herbert Austin was involved in trials of imported tractors, in an attempt to increase food production. By 1917 he had the first prototype of his own design at work. Serious production started in 1919. By 1922 a reduction of import duty allowed imported Fordsons to eat into the British market. Production was later transferred to France.

It was not until Austin merged with Morris to form BMC in the early 1950s, that they became involved with tractors again, this time with Nuffields.

Stiff competition from imported Fordsons and the demands of the booming car business made the Austin a short-lived design.
Eric Sawford

The Gray

Built in Minnesota, the Gray was a good idea that eventually failed. A cross-mounted engine drove two wide rear wheels. By mounting the two wheels close together the track was fairly narrow. When ploughing this allowed both wheels to give a better grip when working on unploughed land . On cultivation work they acted like a roller breaking clods. Tractors of this design sold from 1912 to 1925.

Vintage collectors have imported several makes that were never originally sold in Britain. This unusual 1920 Gray is one of these. Their decline was probably due to the improvement of other tractors rather than a poor original design. A. F. Porter

Hart Parr 18-36

In 1901, Hart Parr were early-starters in tractor production in Iowa. In 1907 they coined the name 'tractor' and in 1912 'farm tractor'. By the 1920s they had earned a reputation for building rugged tractors. With the slump in 1929 they joined with Nichols & Shepherd to form the tractor division of the Oliver Farm Equipment Corporation. The 18-36 was a typical prairie-type tractor intended for driving threshing machines as well as being used for cultivation work.

A few 18-36 were imported to Britain but none are thought to have survived. This is a relatively recent import. Eric Sawford

Saunderson

The Saunderson tractor was produced at Elstow in Bedfordshire. The firm had specialised in mechanical weed-cutting punts. They could hardly fail to be aware of the work of Dan Albone. Built on a channel frame the wheelbase was much longer than strictly necessary to give stability. This must have been one of the few tractors where the driver could not complain of a small toolbox.

Saundersons were soon outclassed, but in their heyday they enjoyed export sales — particularly to Canada. A number survived into preservation having been used as stationary engines driving barn machinery. Fierce competition from Fords among others led to several financial restructurings before production petered out in the 1920s.

The Saunderson compared well with early American imports. The simple and sturdy design was well thought out. Eric Sawford

Walshe & Clarke Victoria Ploughing Engine

The first use of mechanical power for cultivating land was with cable ploughing. The implement was hauled backwards and forwards by two steam engines fitted with winches. Most ploughing engines were exported, although some were operated by contractors in Britain.

Walshe & Clarke of Guiseley felt that an internal combustion engine would offer contractors important advantages: less coal and water to carry, ready for work more quickly and fewer men would be needed to attend to the engines.

They styled their offering like a steam engine. Even the exhaust blast pulled cooling air up the chimney. The manufacturer's timing was unfortunate. By 1922 farming was in decline, following World War 1 prosperity and second-hand steam ploughing engines could be bought cheaply.

Walshe & Clarke were not the only makers to misread the market. Fowler also produced a few diesel ploughing engines. Some contractors actually converted existing steam ploughing engines to diesel operation. Within a few years one crawler tractor and driver could undertake most jobs that needed a whole ploughing team.

This Walshe & Clarke Victoria ploughing engine, which in this example is missing its massive winch, is still undergoing restoration. Eric Sawford.

International Junior

International Harvester was already an established American manufacturer of agricultural machinery. Naturally they added tractors to their product range. Their early tractors were various large and short-lived designs. In 1917 the Model 8-16 Junior was introduced to meet the demand for smaller and cheaper tractors.

Whilst it may appear crude by today's standards it proved an effective tractor. With the 10-20 Titan the Junior was sold in large quantities.

The Junior marked International's arrival as a major tractor manufacturer. One disadvantage was the exposed final drive to the wheels. Dust and stones in the chain caused excessive wear. The starting handle is at the side. The slope to the bonnet is caused by mounting the radiator between the engine and the driver. Driver visibility was improved and this Junior is still ploughing well.
Eric Sawford

Farmall F12

Developing the Farmall concept in 1924 gave International a lead in the competition. By making a tractor high and with a three-wheeled layout it proved ideal for working between rows of standing crops. The spacing of the rear wheels could be adjusted to fit between the rows. Originally designed for corn (maize) growers it led to many other makers adding the same type of tractor to their range.

Other American tractor makers were quick to produce row crop versions as well. Such tractors eliminated weeks of back-breaking toil in the fields with a hand hoe.

On this F12 from the mid-1930s you can see how the steering column went right along the top of the engine. It linked to a steering box mounted above the radiator. ACB

Farmall M

International retained the McCormick name for some models for marketing purposes. With a smooth-running 4-cylinder engine the Farmall M quickly and deservedly earned itself a good reputation.

Underneath the styling it was a larger version of the F12 (on page 25) but with optional wide front axle. International started British manufacture in 1948 with the M re-badged the BM (British M). It is interesting to see the similarities with the later BWD 6, on page 27.

This wartime Farmall M pictured was another Lend Lease model sure of a warm welcome on any farm to which it was allocated. This tractor lay neglected for 30 years before restoration.
ACB

McCormick BWD 6

Responding to duties imposed on imported tractors International 'L' started manufacturing in Britain. The big tractor in their production programme tended to be an American design.

In 1984 Case and International merged to form the Case IH range which is still in production today.

The bonnet on this BWD 6 demonstrates how the power train could be built as a Farmall version as well. The swelling half way down the bonnet is the instrument panel. This is the point where the Farmall steering column would have disappeared under the added sheet metal styling. ACB

Case 20-40

Much of early American tractor design was geared to the large expanses of the Prairies. Direct ploughing had previously been possible with steam traction engines, but constant supplies of water were needed. Many of the first successful tractors were based on steam practice.

One big difference was in the starting. A steamer started as soon as steam was admitted to the cylinders. Imagine the daunting task of pulling over the 17.5litre engine of this 1916 Case 20-40 on a cold morning. The job had to done using a ratchet lever fitted to the crankshaft. Case boasted a special catch which was fitted to protect the driver if the engine backfired.

Another option was 'an enclosed cabin'. Crude though such tractors look they were instrumental in breaking up vast areas of what is now productive land. Their other main job would be driving the threshing machine. Although they were far too large for British conditions they did bring 'new lands' into production to compete with British cereal farmers.

Several of these early machines have been imported in the last few years by collectors. A. F. Porter

Case 22-40

Weighing in at 4.5 tonnes the Case 22-40 was 1 ½ tonnes lighter than its predecessor but could achieve 29 drawbar horsepower on test compared with 24 horse power. Yet both engines developed the same power at the belt pulley. The power gain came from the reduced rolling resistance of the lighter tractor and improved transmission design. Introduced in 1919 this model ran until 1929.

These two number ratings were a guide to the amount of horsepower an early tractor could deliver at the drawbar and the greater power that the engine could apply to driving a machine by belt.

This side view shows how much more compact the design had become. The red 'water' tank fed a special water injector to increase power output when working hard. A. F. Porter

Case Cross Motor

Gradually Case design became more refined. The belt pulley fitted right on the end of the crankshaft and was supported by an outer bearing. This was a great advantage when much of a tractor's life would be spent as a stationary power source. By the end of the 1920s this type of construction was beginning to seem heavy and awkward. At this time all tractors ran on steel wheels and top speed would be no more than a steady walking pace.

This is a late example of the heavyweight Case 'cross motor'. This design had given good service. In use the steel wheels would have lugs bolted on to give extra grip. In the background can be seen the styled Case look introduced in 1939. A. F. Porter

Case L

The L was a completely new model for 1938. While the engine position appeared conventional the rugged transmission was driven by a bevel gear and the final drive was by enclosed roller chains. A British importer was established before the outbreak of war and with the outbreak of war the Case name was destined to become even better known.

This Case L dates from that prewar period. On many farms a tractor-driven circular saw was essential for preparing 'free' heating fuel. ACB

Case LA and DEX

The allocation of all tractors was soon strictly controlled. Permits to acquire were issued by the 'War Ags' (County War Agricultural Executive Committees) that supervised all aspects of food production. Imagine the excitement of both farmer and tractor driver if they were allocated one of these Lend/Lease Cases. Their smooth-running engines provided a contrast to the rougher running of a Fordson.

The Case LA (left) was a styled version of the L. Startled owners used to complain about the alarming fuel consumption of an LA but overlooked the fact that it was twice as powerful as a Fordson. The DEX (right) was a special Case variant for the British Market. Like the Case LA the final drive was still worked by enclosed chains instead of gears. ACB

Case Maxxum 5100 series

Case withdrew from the British market after the war. In 1972 David Brown Tractors was purchased by Case's parent company Tenneco. They recognised that the two makes were complementary. In particular there were British farms big enough to use American-built Case tractors.

The Case IH 5140 is part of the current Maxxum range with unequal sized four-wheel drive. Like its competitors, driver comfort is now a high priority. Many of the controls are electronic and an optional radar meter measures actual travel speed over the ground. This can be used to deduce wheel spin and take steps if it is excessive.

It is at big events, where farmers gather, that tractor salesmen like to demonstrate/display their machines to tempt farmers to re-equip. Despite developing two to three times the power of the Case 20-40 (page 28), this 5140 would be classed as a medium-sized general purpose tractor today. A dealer's static display awaits potential customers. Eric Sawford

Case 7130

Despite its size the hydraulics on the Case 7130 use the same principals laid down by Harry Ferguson over 60 years ago, except the loads are much heavier.

Very different is the sophistication of the controls with a choice of 24 speeds and power-shift to allow gear-changing on the move. Electronic instrumentation and sophisticated controls on the hydraulics all make the driver's job less tiring. Weighing 8 tonnes this Magnum is 2 tonnes heavier than the 20-40 but develops five times the power.

Ploughing is a job that can load down any tractor. The Case 7130 is pulling a reversible plough. At the end of the field it can be lifted out of work and turned over to throw the next furrows in the opposite direction. Peter Adams

Waterloo R (the Overtime)

Probably one of the most influential tractor designs was the Waterloo Model R. Introduced in 1914, it was built by the Waterloo Gasoline Engine Company, Iowa. It was sold in Britain as the 'Overtime'. From their base in Smithfield, London, the Overtime Tractor Company promoted the make vigorously. As a result of trials and demonstrations it became widely known.

It marked the arrival of a relatively mass-produced and reliable tractor. As a result it became the target that other newer tractors had to beat. The demands on farming caused by World War 1, made it possible for progressive farmers to at least consider purchasing a tractor. Various other imported tractors were available in small numbers and businessmen sensed that there could be a commercial future for tractors. John Deere ensured the company's lasting success by buying the company in 1918.

The simple design of the Waterloo included a stationary engine driving the rear wheels, all mounted on two steel channels.
A. F. Porter

John Deere A

During World War 2, Lend Lease was a form of American assistance which enabled the British Government to acquire equipment for the war effort. This lead to the arrival of many John Deere tractors. Not only had Deere continued to develop its designs from the original Waterloo; these tractors had styling. Most were high-clearance row crop types. Despite their unfamiliar horizontal two-cylinder engine layout they quickly gained a good reputation. As well as being robust such an engine meant the tractors could run on poor fuel. Starting was by grasping the flywheel and pulling smartly.

Postwar dollar shortages meant that new John Deeres were not available in Britain from the end of the 1940s. One independent engineer persisted in offering spares and servicing which allowed many farms to keep existing machines running.

This 1948 Model A would have been one of the last of the imports and is typical of the tractors many potato growers relied on for cultivation.
Eric Sawford

36

John Deere BR

Another reminder of wartime John Deeres is the BR. The same two-cylinder layout as the 'A' is used but with smaller cylinders. This was built as a 'Regular' rather than a 'Row Crop' tractor.

The ease with which these vehicles could tow implements such as binders highlighted the advantages of tractor power. A horse-drawn binder represented hard slogging work for two or three horses. The mechanism was driven by a ground wheel so there was a constant heavy load. With summer sun beating down on them no team could cope with more than a few hours of unrelenting toil. In contrast the tractor could work at the same pace all day without strain to man or machine. Most problems came from horse binders being shaken to pieces by enthusiastic drivers towing them too fast.

Horses still have a number of 'design advantages' over tractors especially when money is tight. Their 'fuel' can be grown on the farm. A farmer can breed his own replacements. A well-trained horse will respond to voice commands and will move forward and stop without anybody at the 'controls'. After several years training on farm work a good six year old horse can be sold at a profit for work in town.

As motor vehicles replaced horses, especially during the 1930s, the value of a good horse dropped. This reduced the profits to be earned breeding and training horses. The purchase of a tractor became a better financial proposition. Even today there are few farmer-enthusiasts who can still make an economic case for using real horses rather than horsepower.

A wartime John Deere BR with its binder. ACB

John Deere 710

The Lanz factory at Mannheim, Germany was purchased in 1956 by John Deere as a foothold in Europe. Lanz semi-diesels had a fine reputation as rugged long-lasting designs. Even with electric starting they were beginning to seem rather old-fashioned. Manufacture of existing models continued, painted in John Deere livery. New designs were soon under development. The plant became Deere's source world wide for smaller tractors in the range.

Pictured is a 50hp 710. This short-lived (1965/6) model proved Mannheim's quality of building. ACB

John Deere 4450

By the time Deere returned to the British market in the late 1960s, they were offering high horsepower tractor with six-cylinder diesel engines. These found a market with farmers requiring powerful tractors able to work fast. Driver comfort is important in order to obtain high output and John Deere cabs were the first to feature tinted windows, sound-proofing, radio and tape player, and air conditioning. Many tractor drivers have commented that the cab on their John Deere is more comfortable than their sitting room. If driver comfort means the ploughing gets completed before the weather breaks many farmers would feel it was justified. Mind you, one early John Deere customer insisted the 'included in the price air conditioning' was removed before his tractor was delivered. Instead he had it fitted to his car.

This 4450 from the mid-1980s uses its power and grip ploughing in Oxfordshire. Peter Adams

John Deere 7800

Deere is still a well-established and innovative manufacturer of tractors and agricultural and industrial machinery. Its colour scheme of green relieved by yellow has lasted unchanged.

Many American farmers do not employ any labour so feel that they deserve a comfortable working environment. A high specification cab makes long hours at the wheel more acceptable. This pattern is repeating itself in Britain.

For years engineers have been predicting 'tractors of the future' that would be controlled by a farmer sitting in an armchair in his farm office. Instead, with the spread of mobile phones and lap-top computers it is now quite possible to conduct farm office work whilst cultivating a field. The only difference is that the office and armchair are in the tractor cab travelling across the field.

This 7800 waiting to be demonstrated by a dealer, is typical of current Deere production. It certainly forms a contrast with the Waterloo R of 80 years ago. Practical demonstration is still the best way of showing that these big tractors can get the job done. The weight of the six furrow reversible plough is counterbalanced by extra detachable weights attached to the frame under the headlights. Eric Sawford

Fordson N & E27N

Farmer's son Henry Ford was appalled by the drudgery of farm life. Having become a successful car maker he began experimenting with tractor designs. In 1917 his first customer was the British Government who ordered the first 5,000 to be built. These were needed to mechanise farming towards the end of World War 1. Ford believed in mass production. Ford ceased production in the United States in 1928, transferring production briefly to Cork, Ireland, then as soon as the new purpose-built factory at Dagenham was ready, production was transferred once again, to Essex.

History repeated itself in 1939 when the Fordson proved once again that it was vital for food production in World War 2. The majority of tractors supplied to wartime agriculture poured from the modern Ford plant at Dagenham. Compared with imported machines they were basic but they got the work done. All sorts of people were rapidly converted to Fordson drivers, from schoolboys to Duchesses.

In front is a 1939 Fordson N in the short-lived orange livery. Behind is a postwar E27N Fordson Major, with the welcome luxuries of electric starter and lighting, for working after nightfall. ACB

Roadless Conversion

The Roadless Company of Middlesex specialised in modifying vehicles for work under difficult conditions. Many Fordson 'Ns' were modified by them (and other convertors) to produce specialised machines. It meant all the basic mechanical spare parts would be widely available.

Roadless went on to specialise in converting Fordson tractors to crawlers or four-wheel drive.

This converted Fordson N is typical of Roadless's crawler winch tractors. In wartime they would be on stand-by for aircraft recovery and general winching duties on grass airfields. As well as steering, the front wheels supported the winch. Eric Sawford

Auto Mower Timber Trailer

Auto Mower of Frome, Somerset manufactured heavy duty winch outfits for timber extraction. Often the same outfit would be used to haul the trailer to the sawmill, a long and slow journey. It could have replaced either a steam engine or a team of horses. A number of established timber-fellers keep some of their old tackle about the yard. Cynics say it is to remind themselves how much easier the has been made with modern machinery. Secretly many will admit to sentimental reasons. Following several books by Maurice Sanders, on the exploits of timber men, there has been increased interest preserving timbering machinery.

A fine example of an Auto Mower heavy duty winch outfit for timber extrzction. Power comes from a 1934 Fordson N. The additional chassis and non-standard wheels are to ease the stress of winching out round timber. Eric Sawford

43

Fordson Major E27N

The urgent need for tractors meant that the E27N Major, introduced in 1945 had to retain the obsolete Fordson side-valve engine. It did gain a more efficient transmission. The revised driving position earned it the nickname of the 'High Major'.

During its production run the design gradually gained the options of electric starting, lights, power take off, and hydraulic linkage. The option of a factory-fitted Perkins P6 diesel engine from 1948 offered greater power and many Majors were later repowered with Perkins Engines.

Illustrated is a row crop version of the E27N Major with electric starting. Fords still installed a starting handle to save the battery. Electric starting made the driver's job less physically demanding. It also reduced the temptation to leave the tractor idling. The trailer on tow would originally have been pulled by a traction engine. ACB

Ford 8N

Following Henry Ford's retirement in 1945 Harry Ferguson fell out with the Ford Motor Company. His design had certainly proved itself though. Ford continued to manufacture tractors incorporating Ferguson designs. This led to long legal action by Harry Ferguson against Ford. The eventual outcome was partial victory for Harry Ferguson. A partial redesign followed and a change of colour. These American-built Fords were not supplied to England but were supplied to other parts of Europe.

Imported from Ireland this Ford 8N is a rare sight at a British tractor rally. ACB

Fordson New

The 'New' Fordson Major created a sensation when launched in 1952. At last Ford had been able to add a new engine to the improved transmission introduced on the E27N Major. The diesel engine was a ready starter even in cold weather and most tractors were ordered as diesels.

Here, the Major (left) has gained a six-cylinder Ford engine as an unofficial modification. (The transmission was robust enough to handle the extra power.) The 1930s N next to it is hidden by the early 1960s Fordson Super Major. The only maker causing Ford real concern was Ferguson (far right). This example dates from 1949 but has been fitted with a Perkins P3 engine for extra power and greater fuel economy. Such conversions were very popular and eventually gave Ford an idea. ACB

Fordson Dexta

The Dexta was powered by a Perkins 3-cylinder diesel engine disguised as a Fordson product. It was introduced in 1958 to offer Fordson dealers a smaller and cheaper tractor to sell. Apart from the six speed transmission it was clearly inspired by the result of fitting a Perkins P3 engine to a Ford Ferguson. It proved a very willing worker and many are still in daily use on farms.

Many makes of tractor have been fitted with engines made by Perkins of Peterborough. Although owned by Massey Ferguson since 1958 this trend continues. The founder Frank Perkins was a steam man, being a director of Aveling & Porter. When they ran into financial trouble he returned to Barford and Perkins, the family company. There he started making lightweight diesel engines. In 1937 the P6 was announced. Once World War 2 was over they specialised in supplying engines to operators to replace existing power units and to manufacturers keen to offer a diesel option for their trucks, buses, tractors and plant. P engines were made in 3, 4 and 6-cylinder versions and had a distinctive 'rattling' engine note.

The Dexta as a compact but powerful tractor is lightly loaded pulling only two furrows. Eric Sawford

47

County and Roadless

Ford Tractors also formed the raw material for specialist converters. County Commercials of Fleet started by adding extra axles to Fordson lorries. After World War 2 they produced a neat tracklayer conversion of the E27N. This continued with the 'New' Major. Their four-wheel drive conversions came later and always featured equal-size wheels. In some cases Ford six-cylinder engines were fitted to increase pulling power. Roadless Traction was introduced on page 42. Their four-wheel drive conversions normally featured smaller wheels on the front axle. Both companies lost sales when Ford started offering factory-built high horsepower four-wheel drive tractors.

The County (right) is converted from Fordson Super Major whilst the Roadless is based on the later Ford 5000. ACB

Doe Triple D

When faced with stiff Essex clay to plough, plenty of power is needed. Mr G. Prior reasoned the cheapest method was to link two Fordson Majors together. This idea was developed by Ernest Doe the local Fordson Dealers and sold as the Triple D (Doe's Dual Drive).

To drive, the combination was far more agile than it looked. By hydraulic power the whole front tractor could be pivoted to pull the outfit round. The controls on the front tractor were operated by a mixture of bowden cables and hydraulic slave cylinders. The big disadvantage of this design showed itself when pulling out of blind turnings. The tractor nearly blocked the road before the driver could check it was clear. Many Triple Ds were converted back to two tractors later in life so survivors are not very common. They paved the way for today's high horsepower tractors.

Incorporating two Super Majors this Triple D (left) was built in the early 1960s. In contrast (right) is a pedestrian-operated Trusty Tractor made 20 years earlier. A. F. Porter

Ford 8210

The 8210 110hp 4x4 was the biggest British-built Ford of the 1980s. Here the power is being used both to drive the forage harvester picking up the grass and to pull the trailer it is being blown into. For this job the power and the grip eliminates the need for an extra tractor to run alongside with the trailer. It is savings like this that make it possible to justify buying bigger and more powerful tractors. Peter Adams

Ford FW30

Low prices for crops have meant that many American farms are now run without hired labour. As a result the farmer and his family may work long hours on their tractors during planting time. At the same time implements with big working widths have been developed that require a lot of power. To meet these needs a number of specialist tractor builders started making super tractors that were far more powerful than those offered by the large companies. Many of the components came from earth-moving machinery for their robustness.

Initially they were bought because it made it possible for farmers to get their planting done quickly. Under British conditions they were used to replace crawler tractors. Typically they would be expected to pull a string of several narrower implements to cultivate the soil in one pass. A few farmers are importing individual big tractors for their own use. As a result sometimes unfamiliar big tractors can be seen at work on arable farms. Their large size makes it impractical to move them far on public roads. Once again, it took a new small company to show the major manufacturers where demand was heading. These tractors should be lightly stressed and American users are predicting they will have to last for 20 years or more to be economic.

Despite its badges this 8-wheeled giant was bought in from Steiger for resale as a Ford. The cultivator at the rear was working deep to break up the pan that can form in the soil — below ploughing depth — and can restrict plant growth. Peter Adams

Ford TW Range

Tractors supplied from the American plants brought more powerful options to British users. High horsepower is useful for hauling heavy loads as trailers get bigger. Specialist self-propelled machines have a fast rate of work. This demands a team of powerful tractor and tipping trailer combinations to work alongside. Their task is to get the trailers emptied, where the cut grass will be stored for winter feed. Once tipped they need to get back to the field so as not to hold up the forage harvester.

Following the takeover by Fiat, the Ford name is being phased out in favour of 'New Holland'. The latest designs are now shared between the New Holland and Fiat ranges. This is part of the world-wide trend for fewer and bigger tractor manufacturers. Each plant world-wide can concentrate on producing a limited range of tractors in quantity. Yet users have a wide choice of specification. His dealer can offer this from a wide range of tractors sourced from the various plants.

For the highest output this self-propelled forage harvester is cutting, precision chopping and blowing the grass into the trailer at the rate of several tonnes a minute. Peter Adams

Belarus 1507

The Russian tractor industry started in the 1920s manufacturing Fordsons in two factories supplied by Henry Ford. For a time 85% of all Russian tractors were based on Fordsons. Russia has long been self-sufficient in home-designed tractors. Limited numbers were exported under the Belarus name. World-wide they have a reputation as rugged and old-fashioned designs but are good value at their low selling prices.

Extreme cold in winter means starting can be difficult. On this 1507 Turbo four-wheel drive a small two-stroke petrol engine is used to rotate the main engine until it fires. Eric Sawford

Fowler Gyrotiller

Originally designed for cultivating sugar cane plantations the Fowler Gyrotiller was a powered digging machine. Introduced in 1932 it could work to a remarkable half a meter depth. It seemed a logical successor to Fowler's steam ploughing outfits. Elsewhere it was not too successful as the cultivated soil was left rather hollow and crops tended to dry out. Most were powered by Fowler-built diesel engine. Ironically after the Gyrotillers went out of production in 1937 they proved ideal for reclaiming neglected land for food production during World War 2. This was the first example of applying engine power direct to the cultivating machinery rather than dragging it through the soil.

Below: *is the largest version, the massive 170hp model. With a working width of 3 meters (10 feet) and an overall width of 3.5 meters only a substantial contractor could afford such a major capital investment.* Eric Sawford

Right: *A considerable proportion of the available engine power was needed to turn these two digging heads.* A. F. Porter

Fowler Crawler

Fowler started in Leeds as agricultural engineers making steam cable ploughing engines. By the time they moved into tractor manufacture they had a high reputation; as the demand for steam declined they started manufacturing diesel crawler tractors. With their background they were rugged and powerful. Unfortunately they did not prove to be very profitable. Once their engine problems were corrected they realised that there was more potential in making engines. After a brief period as a nationalised tank factory during the war they eventually came into common ownership with Marshall and resumed making crawlers.

Fowler Crawlers of the 1930s were ruggedly built and quite stylish in appearance. This is one of the few survivors. ACB

Marshall M

Marshall of Gainsborough had built and exported some 30hp 'Agricultural Oil Motors' by 1910. It was not until they were faced with declining demand for their steam engines that Marshalls turned to manufacturing true diesel tractors in the 1930s. They felt their customers needed a strong basic and economical to run tractor. Inspiration came from the Lanz Bulldog, a German semi-diesel tractor. By using a big bore single cylinder two-stroke engine they achieved a simple design with great lugging power. The Marshall M found a market with customers who needed more power than other tractors could provide. The cheap fuel helped to offset the high capital cost. The availability of a factory-fitted winch meant that many Ms were used for timber hauling or by threshing contractors.

Starting the Marshall M pictured was heavy work. After unscrewing a plug in the cylinder head a lighted slow-burning touch paper was inserted. After four vigorous turns of the massive starting handle the engine hit compression and fired. If it backfired the starting handle could easily throw the luckless driver through the air!
A. F. Porter

Field Marshall Series II

Post World War 2 the Marshall M was restyled and christened the Field Marshall. Even after the restyling, driver comfort was still a very low priority. Shaken in his seat by every firing stroke of the engine the driver was sprayed with drops of used lubricating oil from the exhaust pipe via the fly wheel. Carbon would build up in the exhaust when lightly used. Heavy work then led to a chimney fire, showering hot cinders on the luckless driver.

One improvement was a novel additional starting system. With the controls correctly set a special blank cartridge could be inserted and detonated to start the engine. The first series of Field Marshalls had a differential lock. This prevented one drive wheel spinning if it lost traction. Marshalls dropped this feature after a few years. It was another 10 years before other makers offered 'diff locks'. Now they are a standard feature on most tractors offering increased traction in sticky conditions.

Despite its faults there were few tractors to match a Field Marshall for lugging capacity under difficult conditions. Whilst drivers were delighted to get a more comfortable replacement for a Field Marshall most complained that the replacement lacked power.

Illustrated is a Series 2 of 1948. The driving position is based on a flat platform and it would be another 30 years before other makers started to offer flat decks but this time inside cabs.
ACB

Field Marshall Series III

The more gears a tractor has the better chance that the engine will be delivering full power at any particular forward speed. An extra two-speed gearbox doubled the number of ratios to six on a Series III Field Marshall. As a result the engine had to be run in the opposite direction to that of the Series II. Because of their character they are still fondly remembered by drivers and owners. Often these are the same people who changed to multi-cylinder tractors with electric starting as soon as they could be obtained. Marshall eventually disappeared into British Leyland. The name and trade mark was briefly revived in the late 1980s. They were applied to the last of the Leyland tractors as well as few models of imported tractors.

This Series III wears the orange livery adopted by Marshalls to unify the Fowler and Marshall colours. The old-fashioned electric lights were linked to a dynamo but no battery or electric starter was supplied. ACB

Nuffield M4

*'Importing big tractors cost dollars. Dollars
are short. We need a British big tractor. Get
Lord Nuffield (William Morris) to build
them.'* This Government-thinking formed the
background to Morris Motors going into
tractor manufacture. Power came from a well-
proved side-valve unit used in Morris lorries
and gun tractors. Many of the gearbox
components came from the same source.
Machine tools were scarce, so proven
manufacturing techniques made sound sense.

The final result was a British-designed and
built tractor which was a worthy competitor to
imported American tractors. Once in service a
few flaws showed themselves. The high-
revving engine combined with five forward
speeds made the first Nuffields remarkably
fast on the road. The elaborate steering
system soon developed play in the joints.
Together these factors produced unpredictable
steering at high speed. The protruding axles
demolished many a gatepost as they were in
blind spots from the drivers seat.

However, these were minor niggles. Here in
1948 was a tractor that could be started at the
press of a button. A special double carburettor
meant the tractor could be stopped at any time
and restarted on petrol. It was strong and
capable. No wonder early Nuffields were
prized.

*On this early production example the
offending axle shafts have been shortened but
the steering linkage can be seen.* ACB

Nuffield 4/60

Nuffields developed by evolution. After a period offering the option of a Perkins diesel the newly developed 3.4litre BMC lorry diesel was fitted. One great advance in 1957 was the Independent Power Take Off (PTO). On Nuffields with this feature the driver could declutch the tractor or the PTO separately. This allowed a baler, for example, to continue being driven while the Nuffield paused to allow a particularly large mound of straw to be digested. With the PTO declutched tight turns could be made without damaging the drive shaft. The 4/60 illustrated had all these features plus an enlarged 3.8 litre engine and a very responsive mechanical governor.

This example is fitted with a Lambourn tractor cab. Tarpaulin was secured over a simple framework. Air conditioning was provided by draughts! Nevertheless it did provide far more protection than the old army greatcoat favoured by tractor drivers. The steelwork is the mounting for a hydraulic loader.
The Nuffield has always been an underrated tractor.
ACB

The BMC Mini

This was aimed at the same market as the Ferguson 20. The intention was to cater for application where a Nuffield was too big. Much of the design work was done on contract by former Ferguson employees. When it was announced in 1965 the most remarkable feature was the power unit. The 950cc 15hp diesel engine was based on the A series engine used in Morris Minors and Minis. Had that been offered as an option for the cars BMC could have led the trend for small diesel minis. In use the BMC Mini proved under-powered and from 1968 it gained the 1,500cc engine used in certain vans. Its most formidable competitor proved to be a good second hand Ferguson 20 and production had ceased by 1970.

The BMC Mini had strong resemblance to the Ferguson 20. On tow is a converted horse-drawn grass mower. Such conversions provided many of the first implements when a farmer bought a tractor for the first time.
ACB

British Leyland 270

Following various takeovers Morris Motors eventually came under the control of British Leyland. Concerned by poor sales BL decided to rename the well-established Nuffield Tractor business. The most visible early change was to adopt a new blue livery. A major part of their output was skid units (virtually a tractor less wheels) to be built into JCBs. Starved of development funds, their design stagnated and they gradually became outclassed by other makers.

This ingenious use of a 1970s Leyland 270 is by the North Norfolk Railway. The tractor driver controls the position of the flail hedge trimmer whilst the engine driver controls the forward speed. Protection for the driver in the event of overturning was provided by the factory fitted safety cab. ACB

Porsche

Porsche sound an unlikely tractor manufacturer but Dr Porsche designed quite a neat range of air-cooled tractor engines. In the 1950s a few of these Alligaier Porsche tractors were imported by a Gloucestershire company. At that time the Porsche name was mainly associated with contract design work. Germany has been rather late, compared to some countries, in appreciating the interest in old tractors. As a result a number of British collectors have imported German tractors for preservation. In the 1950s many manufacturers in Germany produced small numbers of tractors each year using bought-in major components. As a result some unfamiliar names sometimes appear at rallies.

The guard rail on the mudguard of this example is typical German practice to enable a passenger to be transported from the village to the field. This single cylinder Alligaier Porsche was the smallest of the range. ACB

Ransomes

Ransomes were a versatile Suffolk company famous for their ploughs and threshing machines. To power their threshing machines they built steam engines. A prototype petrol tractor was constructed in 1904 but not pursued. They even went into building trolleybuses for South Africa. With such a varied background it is hardly surprising that in the 1930s they felt there was need for a little crawler tractor for horticultural use. Roadless Traction (see page 49) supplied the rubber jointed tracks.

These handy little machines could even be used inside greenhouses.

Later variations included a dumper for use in waterworks filter beds; a hydraulic loader and an industrial tractor with four equal-sized wheels. This was also steered crawler fashion. Had one been fitted with a hydraulic loader Ransomes could have found themselves inventing skid steer loaders! One of Ransomes demonstrators once towed a fully-laden 8-wheeled tanker two miles to clear a breakdown. Even Ransomes admitted that was asking rather a lot of a 6hp engine. Today Ransomes is owned by a Swedish plough-maker and has much reduced from its heyday.

Illustrated is an MG5 towing a Ransomes trailer plough. ACB

Trac Grip

Ever since the 1930s every few years a company feels that there is need for a specialist agricultural transport vehicle. In many cases the design brief was that it would do the same job as a horse and cart. Common features were: a low-powered engine, tractor-type tyres on the drive wheel(s), tight turning circle, and a top speed under 10mph. Such machines sell in relatively small numbers, but makers come and go. Their unusual designs make them popular exhibits with collectors. Similar machines are still being built today by various firms.

This Trac Grip Mk 2 which dates from 1957 is a typical example built in Callington, Cornwall. ACB

Gunsmith

Ferguson's Casualties. The next group of tractors were short lived makes. They flourished briefly in the period of high demand after World War 2. Then Ferguson supply started to catch up with demand. Many buyers chose a second-hand Ferguson rather than a new small tractor at the same sort of cost. Gradually the demand for new machines faded away.

Gunsmith produced the 'Light Tractor'. It was just about able to plough a single furrow under favourable conditions. It did prove useful for row crop cultivation.

Illustrated (right) is an early example from 1946. Visible behind the driver's seat is the flat belt drive from the engine to the transmission. Drive was only possible when the belt was tensioned. Thus the belt acted as a crude clutch. The Nuffield 4/60 (left) is fitted with a safety frame. This was introduced to offer limited protection to a driver if the tractor overturned. ACB

BMB Plowmate

British Motor Boats (BMB) imported outboard motors from America and later added horticultural tractors. When supplies were unobtainable they started local manufacture.

The 6hp Plowmate shown was the biggest of the range. As its name suggests it could make a reasonable job with a single furrow.

Brockhouse (BMB) President

Pedestrian-operated tractors were hard work for the drivers so there was a demand to ride instead. From this evolved the ride-on President. BMB were taken over by the Brockhouse Group and moved to Southport where the factory had previously manufactured the Vulcan lorry. Their emphasis on lightness meant the President appeared under-powered against competitors. Production petered out in 1956.

As shown, the driver of a President enjoyed a good view from the seat. ACB

OTA

The end of wartime production left many factories and workshops looking for a product to offer. This tended to coincide with a pent-up demand for new equipment. Under these conditions even quite uncommercial designs flourished briefly.

Oak Tree Appliances was formed in 1948 in Coventry. Like the BMB President their tractor was built on a steel frame and used car components. In this case the Ford 10 side-valve engined (BMB favoured the Morris 8). Buyers were offered a choice of three, or four-wheel layout. With sales declining the company was bought by Singer Motors. The OTA became the Singer Monarch until the Rootes Group took over Singers and put an end to tractor production.

An example of the three-wheel layout OTA. ACB

British Anzani Iron Horse

British Anzani started as builders of aircraft engines before World War 1. At the end of World War 2 they were one of the companies that felt there was a market for a basic pedestrian-operated tractor.

The 6hp petrol engine could roughly match the work rate of a good horse. A belt pulley at the rear could drive stationary machinery. Various implements could be built up on the tool bar. In some ways the 'Iron Horse' was too like its namesake. The driver had to stumble along behind the implement. Lifting the implement was heavy work. At the end of the day the operator was tired out. Despite being cheap to buy most potential customers preferred to ride and bought a 'proper' tractor. Although production ceased in the early 1950s Anzani continued as a property company after a spell making light cars and vans.

Although the Anzani Iron Horse could plough a reasonable furrow, the driver had to work hard. Tony Ash

Ford Ferguson

Ulster farmer's son Harry Ferguson had an obsession. Conventional tractors were far too heavy. Instead he proposed to use his three point linkage to join implement and tractor. This transferred the forces of the soil acting on the implement, to the tractor. The need for heavy construction was eliminated. Having fallen out with David Brown by 1938 he persuaded Henry Ford to build tractors to his design in Detroit. Both Henry Ford and Harry Ferguson had much greater vision than just producing tractors. Both recognised that affordable tractors would increase food production, release labour for other jobs and make it possible to reduce the cost of food. Both believed it was important to keep making their tractors more affordable. Time has proved them right. However you measure it, we spend a far smaller part of our income on food today than say 50 years ago.

Although built much later this International (left) still showed all the characteristics that Ferguson deprecated. It was high, long, heavy and its hydraulic linkage was an afterthought. At first farmers were sceptical that a small tractor such as this Ford Ferguson system (right) could do all that was claimed it could. ACB

Ferguson TE20

Thanks to a vigorous marketing and sales strategy masterminded by Harry Ferguson, his postwar tractor was an immediate success and many were exported. In Britain it marked a revolution. With mounted implements jobs could be done quickly and efficiently. The luxury of a self-starter, worked through the gear lever, saved effort. The fingertip control of the hydraulics replaced tugging on ropes, heaving on levers and winding manual adjusters.

Mass production, by the Standard Motor Co, often topped 500 a week, and kept the purchase price down. Many farm horses were put out of work by the arrival of the 'little grey Fergie'. Once the pent-up demand was satisfied other tractor makers lost sales as customers were able to choose a new or even second-hand Fergie. In 1953 Harry Ferguson sold out to the Massey Harris company. His linkage is still a vital part of most tractors today.

This typical TE20 still has the original closed centre pattern tread rear tyre of the type that would have been fitted new. ACB

Ferguson 20

Despite its compact size the Ferguson could do an excellent job. Most new users were amazed at what they could achieve with this apparently undersize tractor. The seating position took a bit of getting used to. The driver sat astride the gearbox. Only the two footrests were provided for resting the feet. No foot boards were fitted so drivers had to brace themselves like a motorcyclist when crossing rough ground.

Although turning two furrows the clean tyres show that the tractor is experiencing almost no wheelspin. Tony Ash

Massey Ferguson 65

Announced in 1958, the 65 always looked like an overgrown small tractor. A Perkins engine and a six-speed gearbox produced a tractor with twice the power of a Ferguson 20. An optional ground speed Power Take Off allowed implements to be driven at a speed proportional to forward travel. The option of power-assisted steering was a novelty. By still using the Ferguson system it could be built lighter than previous tractors in the same power range. Another innovation was the use of disc brakes which were less affected by water and mud.

The arrival of the 65 enabled Massey Ferguson to compete head on with other makers offering bigger tractors. The new red and grey livery was to become a familiar sight in the future. Tony Ash

Wallis

Confusingly, Jerome Increase Case gave his name to two tractor manufacturing companies. 'Case' tractors were made by the J. I. Case Threshing Machine Co. H. M. Wallis who was J. I. Case's son in law was producing the the 'Wallis' tractor from the J. Case Plow Company virtually next door in Racine, Wisconsin.

From 1913 Wallis tractors were built on the unit principle. On a sturdy chassis made by rolling a piece of boiler plate, the engine and transmission were mounted as a unit. Other innovations were roller bearings to reduce friction in the transmission and the first sprung seat to save the driver from some of the jolting. This light and strong construction influenced many later designs.

The rolled boiler plate chassis can be seen on this pair of 1920s Wallis tractors waiting to be rescued and restored in a John Deere dealership in Saskatchewan, Canada. Their dry prairie climate helps the survival of neglected machinery. Some of this has been imported to Britain and when restored adds variety to vintage displays. Jim Wilkie

Massey Harris 101

In 1928 the makers of Wallis Tractors were bought by the Canadian Massey Harris company. (They promptly sold the Case name to the J. I. Case Threshing Machine Co.) Massey Harris binders were well-known in Britain but little was seen of their tractors until World War 2. Probably due to supply difficulties, a variety of engines was used to power the wartime imports.

This is a typical example of the later Massey Harris wartime deliveries: a 101 seen here doing a satisfactory job in a vintage ploughing competition. Ploughing matches have a friendly origin. When a new farmer moved in, his neighbours would give him a day's ploughing to help make ready for sowing. Every ploughman wanted to be seen to do the best job on the day. The quality of work was excellent. Societies then started to promote ploughing matches and they became the place to see the latest machinery demonstrated. There can be few other occupations where employees use their day off to compete to show the standard of work they are capable of. Many societies now stage vintage classes which enable preserved tractors to be seen at work. Eric Sawford

Massey Harris 744PD

After World War 2 Massey Harris was one of the transatlantic companies who chose to commence tractor manufacture in Britain. Based on the transmission and frame of their 44K, the 744PD was fitted with a Perkins P6 diesel engine. In this form it made a useful towing tractor although at first no hydraulic linkage was available. Many of the first tractors were exported to Africa for use in a scheme to grow groundnuts (peanuts) which eventually failed.

Massey Harris faced a huge demand for their self-propelled combine harvesters. This meant that tractor development had been neglected. Realising this they purchased Ferguson in 1953 and Perkins Engines in 1958.

This 744 PD has gained a more modern tyre tread pattern. Like many locally made trailers this one is mounted on an old complete lorry front axle. ACB

Massey Ferguson 590

Ownership of Frank Perkins Ltd meant that MF had a wide choice of power units for different models. With a choice of gearboxes this made it possible to offer a wide range of two and four wheel drive tractors.

Perkins engines still power many different makes and types of agricultural machinery. Massey Ferguson started offering the option of turbocharged tractors soon after the introduction of the 500 series. Driven by exhaust gases a turbocharger compresses and forces air into the engine. This boosts power output from a given size of diesel engine. Many tractor makers have now followed this route both for extra power and cleaner exhausts. Recognising that tractor cabs magnified engine noise, standards were laid down to limit noise at the driver's ear. The 500 series was fitted with a 'Q' or quiet cab. A better suspension seat absorbed much of the jolting experienced by the driver.

Introduced in 1976 the Massey Ferguson 590 demonstrates what soon became recognisable as the Massey Ferguson style. ACB

Massey Ferguson 3690

With the 3000 series Massey Ferguson started applying electronics to the driving of tractors. The driver no longer had to move a lever to produce a result. Instead, moving a switch or pressing a button is sufficient to instruct the electronics to take the appropriate action. These constantly monitor the tractors performance and make frequent adjustments. This produces the results the driver has asked for. Such precise control can increase the hourly work rate. This is likely to be the trend in tractors in the future. The driver will only make the policy decisions. Once input the electronics will carry out the constant minor adjustments. Warnings will be issued only if the tractor is unable to meet the performance standards set by the driver. As always the aim is to reduce driver fatigue and increase performance.

This 3690 is awaiting the next demonstration to be given by Chandlers, the local Massey Ferguson dealers, at the British National Ploughing Championships in 1992 at Newark. Eric Sawford

Landini

From 1925 Italian manufacturer Landini stuck with horizontal single cylinder diesel engines. Strictly these were semi-diesels. A large casting in the cylinder head had to be preheated with a blowlamp before attempting to start it. Such engines could run on some unlikely fuels. Vegetable oil, creosote and used sump oil could all produce power. Landini management came to realise they could not afford the major investment needed to update their designs, and were eventually taken over by Massey Ferguson in 1960 who quickly updated the range and made Italy the source for small Massey Ferguson crawlers. Landini is once again operating as an independent company.

Featured is a recently imported example from the 1950s. Eric Sawford

Additional Information

Magazines with current news of preservation topics: *Old Glory* covers the vintage preservation movement and includes information on forthcoming rallies and events. Good general introduction to the breadth of the preservation movement. On sale in newsagents or direct from CMS Publishing, Bullimores House, Church Lane, Cranleigh, Surrey. *Vintage Roadscene* is published quarterly and includes occasional articles on tractors. Copies can be obtained from newsagents or direct from Vintage Roadscene Publications Ltd, 40 Fairfield Way, Ewell, Epsom, Surrey KT19 0EF.

The National Vintage Tractor & Engine Club. With members throughout Britain and over 30 meeting points it provides a focus for those interested in tractors over 20 years old. Other specialist or local tractor clubs are also affiliated. Details from National Secretary D. Beeby, Fairview, Church Road, Bickerstaff, Ormskirk, Lancs L39 OEB.

Vintage rallies, steam rallies, tractor road runs, vintage workings or other events encourage collectors and restorers to bring out and display their restored tractors. At most of these events, tractors can be seen in full working order, allowing visitors to experience the sounds of the machinary in motion. Some agricultural shows feature parades of older tractors. At many shows local dealers will be displaying modern tractors for sale.

Information like this tends to change. An SAE to Jim Wilkie at Weylode, Tetbury Road, Old Sodbury, Bristol BS17 6RJ will bring you the latest information and an updated factsheet.